Puzzle Mats

phoenix international publications, inc.

Illustrations: Mattia Cerato, Mike Dammer, Peter Grosshauser, Kevin Kelly

Phoenix International Publications, Inc.
7390 North Lincoln Avenue
Lincolnwood, Illinois 60712

Lower Ground Floor, 59 Gloucester Place
London W1U 8JJ

ISBN: 978-1-4508-2405-7

Manufactured in China.

8 7 6 5 4 3 2 1

VISITORS FROM outer space

Connect the dots to draw the alien spaceship.

Use the code to solve this message.

What kind of pet would an alien get? Draw an alien pet below.

IN THE AGE OF DINOSAURS

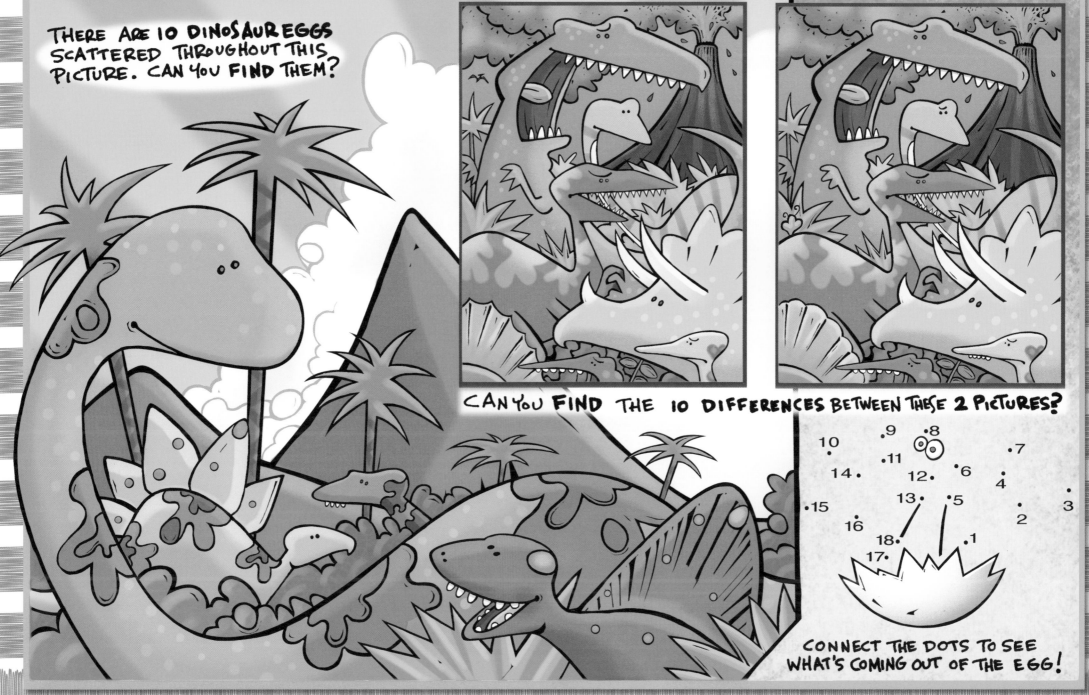

THERE ARE 10 DINOSAUR EGGS SCATTERED THROUGHOUT THIS PICTURE. CAN YOU FIND THEM?

CAN YOU **FIND** THE 10 DIFFERENCES BETWEEN THESE 2 PICTURES?

CONNECT THE DOTS TO SEE WHAT'S COMING OUT OF THE EGG!

Follow the strings to match a Kite with each Kid!

up in the SKY!

Color the scene below!

Help Superdude follow the maze to return the eggs to their nest.

SNAIL RACE

Snails are known for being slow, but this time they are racing against each other! Write their position in the race in the boxes on the left.

CAUGHT IN THE WEB

It's not too late for little fly! Help her find her way through the spider's web to break free.

START

FINISH

CREEPY Crawlies

FLOWER PATH

This butterfly wants to reach the flower. There are three possible paths, but only one takes her there. Which one?

a
b
c

SHOES, SHOES, SHOES!

Wow! This caterpillar needs shoes. How many will he need to buy? Count his feet and circle the right answer, then have fun coloring!

38   40   44

YIKES! THE ANIMALS HAVE TAKEN **LETTERS** FROM **SIGNS** AROUND THE **ZOO**! PLEASE MATCH THE **LETTER** TO EACH **ANIMAL** IN THE **BLANKS** TO ANSWER THIS QUESTION: **WHAT DO DOLPHINS WEAR TO KEEP WARM?**

A Trip to the Zoo

CHANGE ONE LETTER PER WORD TO TRANSFORM THIS **SWEET LITTLE DEER** INTO A **FEROCIOUS LION!!**

DEER

_ _ _ _   TERM OF AFFECTION

_ _ _ _   SHAKESPEARE KING

_ _ _ _   TO REST ON

_ _ _ _   TO LEND MONEY

_ _ _ _   LARGE WATERBIRD

LION

CAN YOU FIND THE **ONE CAMEL** THAT MATCHES THIS **SHADOW** EXACTLY?

A Day at the Museum

BE THE ARTIST
The painter forgot to finish this piece! Help him out and draw what you think suits this scene best!

SAME BUT DIFFERENT
The two paintings are very similar but not the same. Find all 10 differences.

LINK THE DOTS
What is the hidden figure? Link the dots to find out and then color as you like!

MISSING PIECE
Which of the six pieces below is a perfect match to fix this ancient Greek vase?

a b c d e f

SNOW DAY!

Find matching snowflakes around the page, then find the one-of-a-kind snowflake.

Starting at the arrow, follow the letters sideways, down, or diagonally to reveal a winter phrase.

BUILD A SNOWMAN!
Find the following objects in the scene below, then draw them on the snowman: two black eyes, three buttons, carrot, scarf, top hat, two stick arms, six circles for mouth.

L E B Q A
V P T L X
V O I T R E
O I R S I P
U R S I P
K H N O W

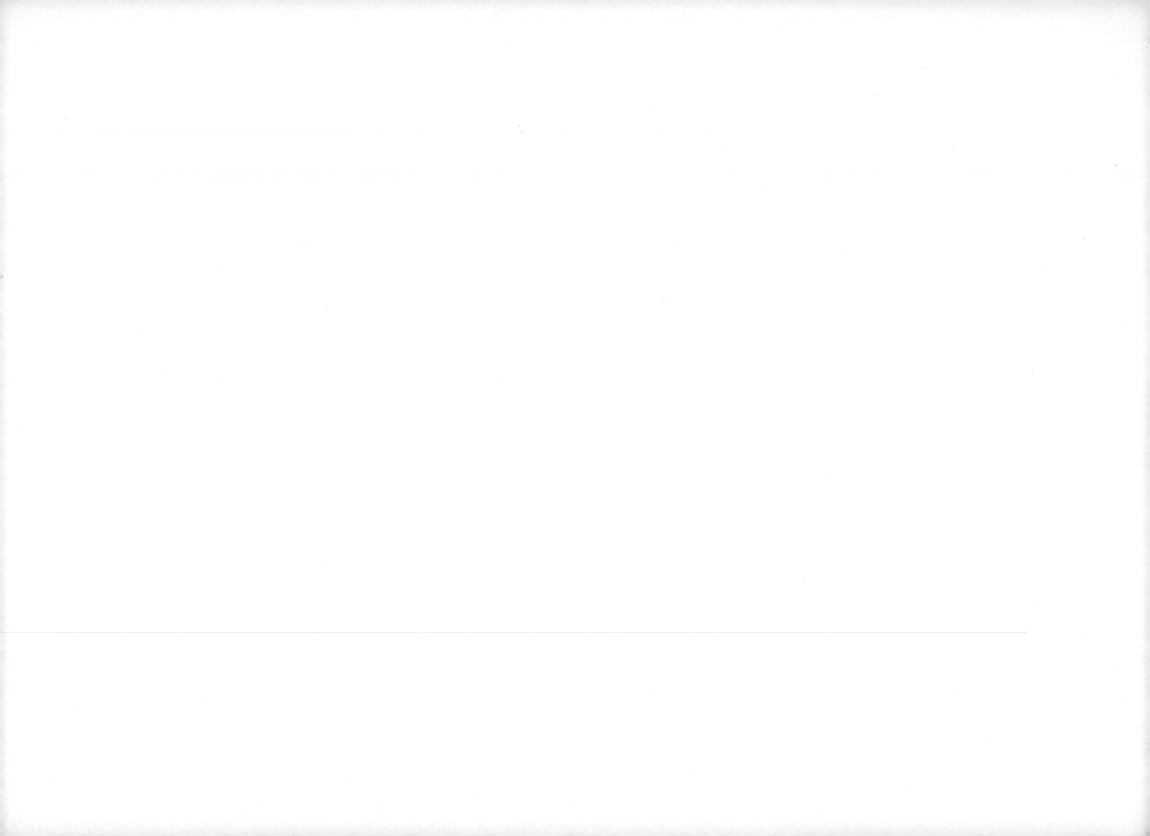

GYM CLASS

ACTIVITIES

Circle 15 gym class activities found below.

A	B	A	S	K	E	T	B	A	L	L	T	R	S
V	L	E	O	V	N	E	Q	U	T	A	G	J	B
O	C	R	F	C	D	N	L	S	F	E	O	O	I
L	B	O	T	R	U	N	N	I	N	G	R	D	S
L	G	B	B	A	R	I	K	F	G	H	K	A	S
E	O	I	A	C	I	S	W	I	M	M	I	N	G
Y	L	C	L	E	I	I	O	O	F	L	C	C	P
B	F	S	L	S	O	C	C	E	R	E	K	I	Z
A	S	F	F	I	D	I	E	D	N	Q	B	N	V
L	S	D	O	D	G	E	B	A	L	L	A	G	J
L	R	H	O	C	K	E	Y	J	G	E	L	O	B
M	D	I	U	E	R	D	F	K	D	G	L	U	S

AEROBICS
BASKETBALL
DANCING
DODGEBALL
GOLF
HOCKEY
KICKBALL
RACES
RUNNING
SOCCER
SOFTBALL
SWIMMING
TAG
TENNIS
VOLLEYBALL

Circle the matching set of tennis rackets.

SCORE

Who scored first? Whoever makes the fewest number of turns on their way to the basket wins!

GO

GO

TREASURE HUNT

Start your quest for ancient riches by jumping from skull to skull! Each skull must have even-numbered teeth and be touching each other. **Be Brave!**

START

Whew! You made it to the treasure trove. There are seven matching pairs of treasure chests. Find them, cross them out, and the one chest remaining is the one filled with treasure. *Yahoo!*

Follow the waterslides to find out which makes it to the end.

the water park

Use letters from the word below to make as many new words as possible:
SPLASHDOWN

WORD SEARCH

Find the following words:
backstroke earplugs summer
cannonball goggles sunscreen
diving innertube swimsuit

```
N W V C E K O R T S K C A B T
Y U Z D Q Q U G U M T W Q D I
Z G H S B L U B O Q G H H I U
W W N O N A A O K G A H B V S
C A N N O N B A L L G G L I M
E B U T R E N N I G O L W N I
U S U N S C R E E N B Y E G W
E A R P L U G S R E M M U S S
```

TOWEL TiC-TAC-TOE

Play with a friend.

There's only one path that leads to the hole. Which one is it, 1, 2, or 3? Help the player find the right one!

Mini Golf

LINK THE DOTS

Who's that cute bird sitting on the tree branch? Connect the dots and find out! Then, color as you like.

RIVER DANGER

The explorer and his guide are traveling along the Amazon, but they don't know the way. Help them find the correct path!

START

FINISH

MONKEY

Only one shadow fits the monkey. Find it!

a b c
d e f

FIND THE DIFFERENCES

Look at the two river explorer illustrations. They are very similar, but they are different in 11 ways. Can you find them all?

AMAZON

RAIN FOREST

Monster Bash

MISSING PIECES
Look around the picture to find hidden objects: beetle, bone, bow tie, brain, flower, peppermint, snail, umbrella, worm

Find all of the words in the list in the letters at the bottom.

start here

GROSS-ERY LIST
broccoli
hairballs
newt
sardines
toadstool
toenails
warts

MONSTER MIRROR
Complete the picture above using the grid to draw a mirror image of the monster.

finish

MONSTER MAZE
Use the maze to find your way from the monster's mouth to his stomach.

```
Y R I A X L E G N T N O
H S A R D I N E S D D M
M N H I Y H R E N Q R V
T M S G J A F P W A W R
B V N R K O P Q C T T P
Y X C U I T Q N B J R N
T L Y L O O T S D A O T
D E P S N G W F L A D E
T O E N A I L S X S D J
S Y I L O C C O R B O Y
S H A I R B A L L S A I
Z S T R A W G R Y T B T
```

Growing Green

Circle the matching watering cans.

Circle the 12 trees.

APPLE	DOGWOOD	MAPLE
ASH	ELDER	OAK
ASPEN	ELM	PINE
BIRCH	LILAC	PLUM

The uncircled letters in order tell what you need to grow trees.

S	D	U	A	S	P	E	N
M	N	O	A	P	L	U	M
A	S	H	G	N	P	E	D
P	I	N	E	W	R	L	A
L	I	L	A	C	O	M	E
E	L	D	E	R	A	O	I
B	I	R	C	H	K	N	D

Which seed goes to which flower? Which stem has the most leaves?

1 2 3

Across the USA

Hint: Which city is called "The Windy City"?

Which two states do not touch any other states?

Unscramble the letters below to spell out the names of seven states.

O L D A C O R O _ _ _ _ _ _ _ _

T U A H _ _ _ _

A R I L F O D _ _ _ _ _ _ _

A G I M C H I N _ _ _ _ _ _ _ _

S A T E X _ _ _ _ _

G E R N O O _ _ _ _ _ _

N O R A Z I A _ _ _ _ _ _ _

Which state is the "Sunshine State"?

Which city is called "The Big Apple"?

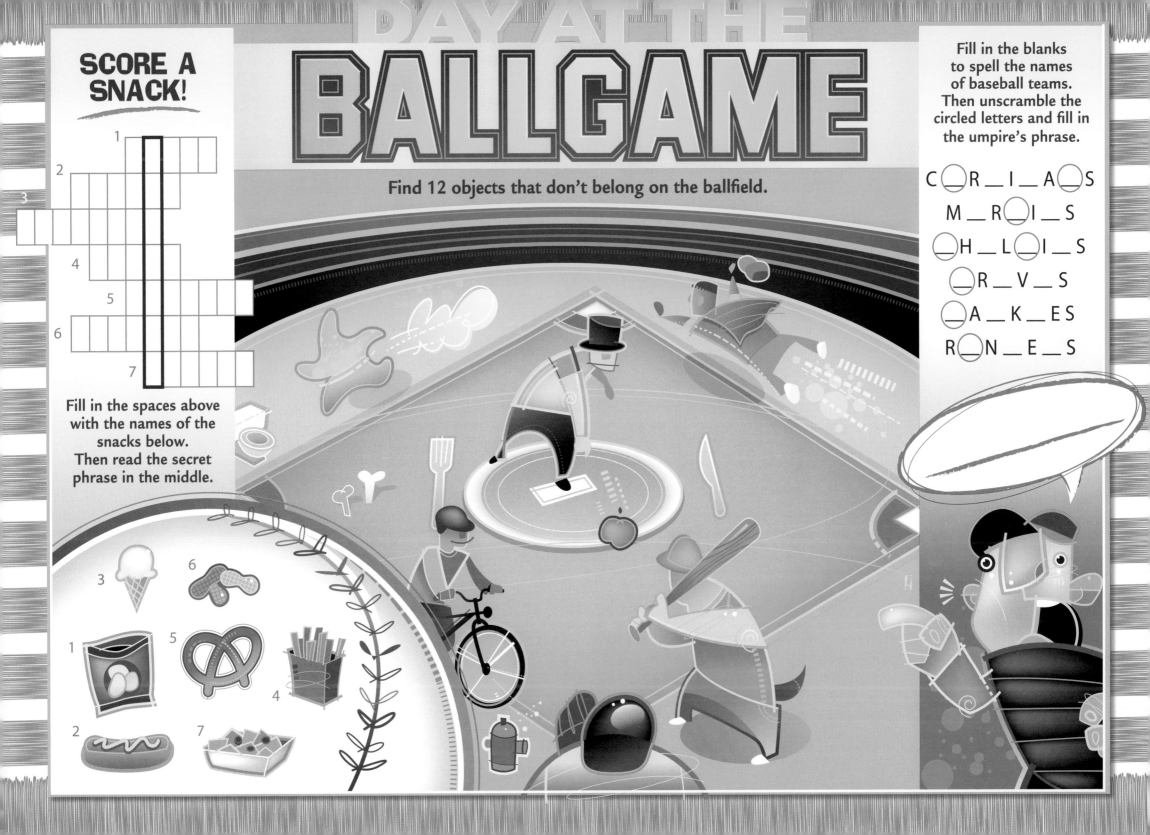

DAY AT THE BALLGAME

SCORE A SNACK!

Fill in the spaces above with the names of the snacks below. Then read the secret phrase in the middle.

Find 12 objects that don't belong on the ballfield.

Fill in the blanks to spell the names of baseball teams. Then unscramble the circled letters and fill in the umpire's phrase.

C◯R__I_A◯S
M__R◯I__S
◯H__L◯I__S
◯R__V__S
◯A__K__ES
R◯N__E__S

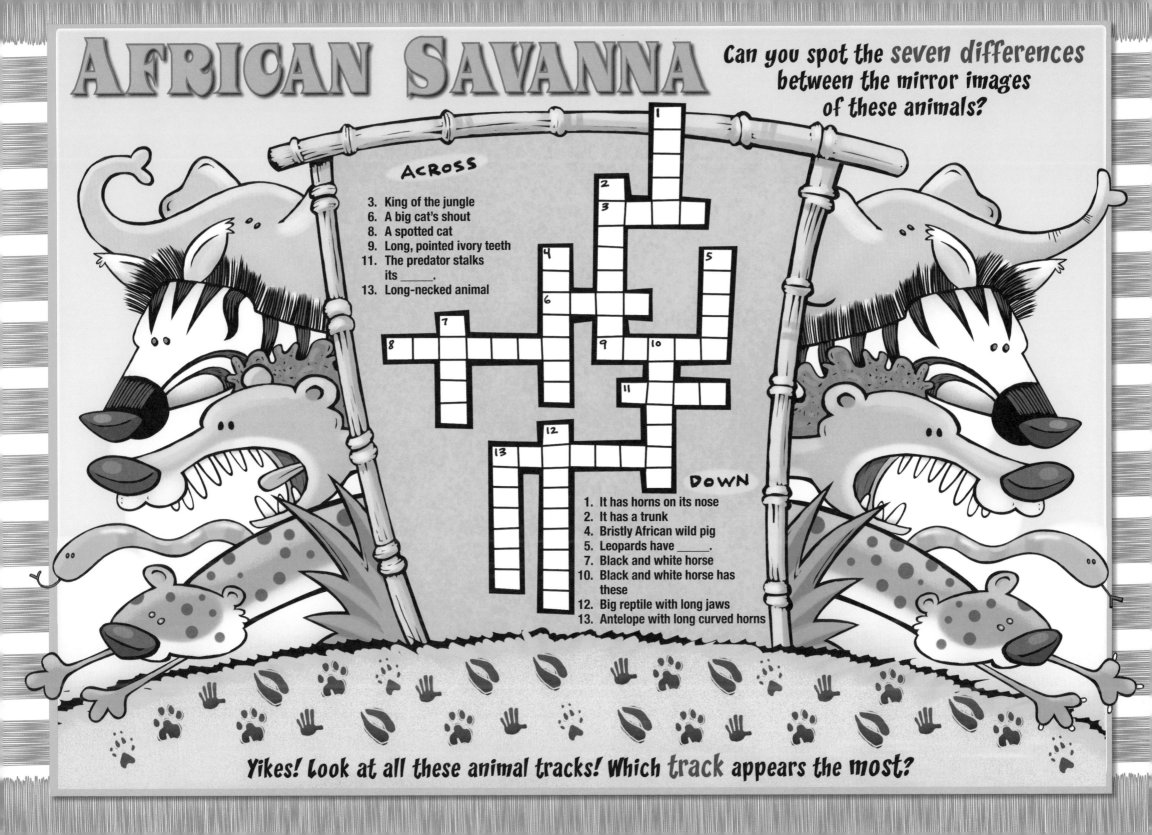

AFRICAN SAVANNA

Can you spot the *seven differences* between the mirror images of these animals?

ACROSS

3. King of the jungle
6. A big cat's shout
8. A spotted cat
9. Long, pointed ivory teeth
11. The predator stalks its _____.
13. Long-necked animal

DOWN

1. It has horns on its nose
2. It has a trunk
4. Bristly African wild pig
5. Leopards have _____.
7. Black and white horse
10. Black and white horse has these
12. Big reptile with long jaws
13. Antelope with long curved horns

Yikes! Look at all these animal tracks! Which *track* appears the *most?*

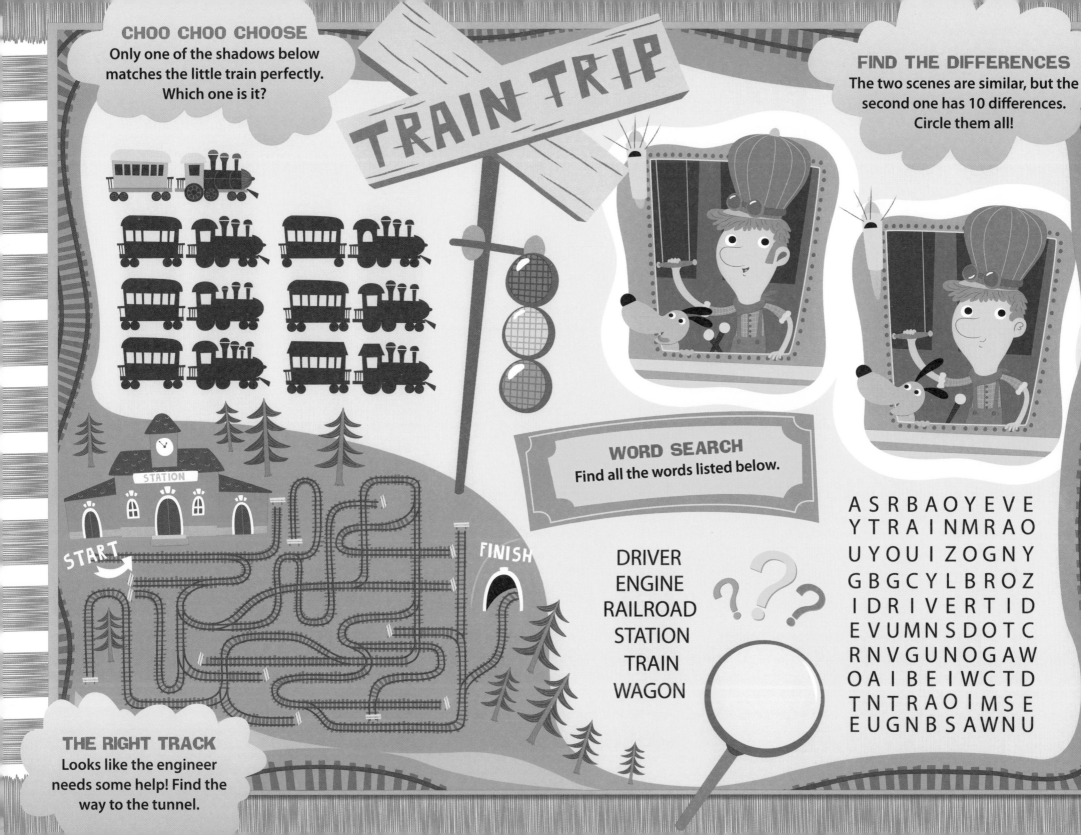

TRAIN TRIP

CHOO CHOO CHOOSE
Only one of the shadows below matches the little train perfectly. Which one is it?

FIND THE DIFFERENCES
The two scenes are similar, but the second one has 10 differences. Circle them all!

WORD SEARCH
Find all the words listed below.

DRIVER
ENGINE
RAILROAD
STATION
TRAIN
WAGON

A S R B A O Y E V E
Y T R A I N M R A O
U Y O U I Z O G N Y
G B G C Y L B R O Z
I D R I V E R T I D
E V U M N S D O T C
R N V G U N O G A W
O A I B E I W C T D
T N T R A O I M S E
E U G N B S A W N U

STATION

START

FINISH

THE RIGHT TRACK
Looks like the engineer needs some help! Find the way to the tunnel.

arcade action!

	1	2	3	4	5
A					
B					
C					
D					

Find the alien invader in each row above that doesn't match the others.

On the picture above, draw only two bridges and one ladder to complete the path and get from the door to the treasure chest.

ladder

bridge

start

end

Starting on the bottom row, jump on **six boxes** on your way to the top. Too easy? The numbers on top of those boxes must add up to **22**!

RODEO FUN

BOOT MAZE
Find your way from start to finish!

START

FINISH

WORD SCRAMBLE
Unscramble the letters below to spell out the correct words!

TSOBO _ _ _ _ _

HESRO _ _ _ _ _

OSLAS _ _ _ _ _

BYOWCO _ _ _ _ _ _

THA _ _ _

DELDAS _ _ _ _ _ _

DIFFERENCES
The two cowboys below are very similar, but there are 11 differences between them. Find and circle them all.

CONFUSING HATS
So many hats!
Only two of them
are exactly the same.
Can you spot them?

TRIP TO NEW YORK

NY Times Crossword
Complete the names in the crossword spaces.

1. ___ State Building
2. ___ Square
3. Statue of ___
4. The Big ___
5. ___way
6. Taxi ___

City Sudoku
Complete the grid below with the four landmarks. Each item should appear only once in every row, column, and square.

Central Park

Empire State Building

Guggenheim

Statue of Liberty

Lost in NYC
Find these objects:
cheese wedge
coffee mug
domino
horseshoe
paintbrush
paper clip
pencil
ship
stoplight

Gridlock
Get each cab to its waiting fare!

Mad for Mexico

Aside from the many beaches, deserts, and mountains, Mexico is also known for its jungles. Unscramble the letters to spell out some animals that can be found in Mexico.

RODIECLOC

_____

RUJAAG

_____

RATPOR

_____

KOMYEN

_____

Can you name the four states that border Mexico?

ACROSS

2. Decorated container filled with candy
3. Favorite sport in Mexico
4. Mexico's capital

DOWN

1. Flatbread made of corn or flour
2. Mexican dollar
5. Vegetable used to make nachos

Did you know chocolate was invented in Mexico? What are your favorite chocolate dishes?

PACIFIC OCEAN

MEXICO

MEXICO CITY

MEXICAN SUDOKU

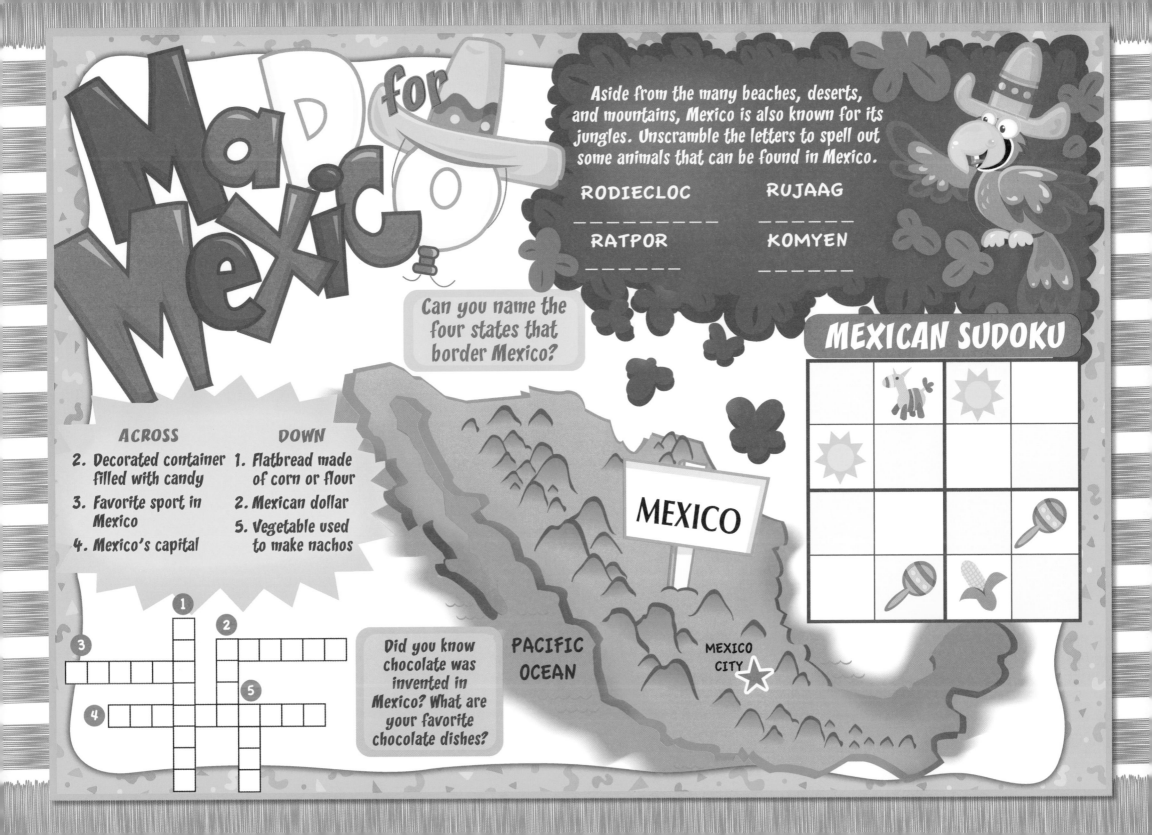

KNIGHTS AND DRAGONS!

```
Q B Q G M X A Q D I Y Q C S
R G S A L R M Y L E Y O J W
F I R E B R E A T H G S D O
C O F D B P V K Z T Q N E R
P H S Q M J T V C C E T I D
X I I Y L K U V H P E V Z W
D L C V Z L O X C M G K T S
S C O N A Y H O Y M P E C A
E M O S P L E G O B M A U M
R C E C T N R B M L L S X G
P D L E I H S Y E E C W P S
E Y B A W E E H S A T O C P
N L W C W Y K U V C Z R O T
T U Q B X S H E U X V R I G
B A L A R M O R V W K A F H
```

ARMOR   CLAW   SERPENT
ARROWS   FIREBREATH   SHIELD
CAVE   HELMET   SWORD
CHIVALRY   SCALES   WINGED

FORSOOTH! FIND THESE WORDS IN THE WORD SEARCH ABOVE!

How many words can you make from the word **DRAGON?**

Hear ye! Hear ye! Unscramble these letters to spell some "medieval" words. Then unscramble the circled letters to answer this riddle:

ZZZZ

Why is Sir George so sleepy?

Because he goes to

_ _ _ _ _ _ _ _ _ _

AELTCS

◯ _ ◯ _ ◯ _ _

TAMO

◯ _ _ ◯ _

GIKN

◯ _ _ _ ◯

IOTNSJUG

◯ _ _ _ _ ◯ ◯ _

ZAZHHU

◯ _ _ _ _ ◯

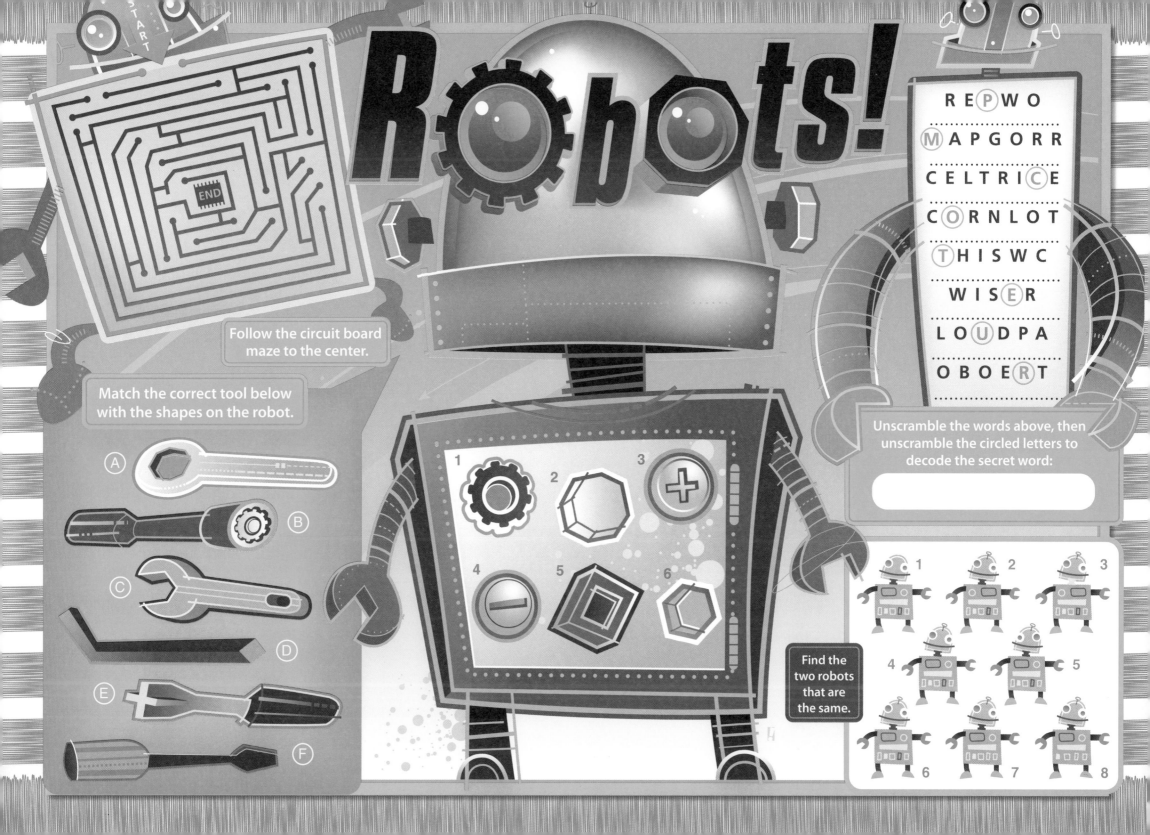

Robots!

Follow the circuit board maze to the center.

START

END

Match the correct tool below with the shapes on the robot.

Ⓐ
Ⓑ
Ⓒ
Ⓓ
Ⓔ
Ⓕ

1
2
3
4
5
6

R E P W O
M A P G O R R
C E L T R I C E
C O R N L O T
T H I S W C
W I S E R
L O U D P A
O B O E R T

Unscramble the words above, then unscramble the circled letters to decode the secret word:

Find the two robots that are the same.

1 2 3
4 5
6 7 8